# Double Bind?

for violin & electronics

Score

Boosey & Hawkes Music Publishers Ltd
www.boosey.com

Published by Boosey & Hawkes Music Publishers Ltd
Aldwych House
71–91 Aldwych
London
WC2B 4HN

www.boosey.com

ISMN 979-0-060-12824-0
ISBN 978-1-78454-087-6

First published 2014. This impression 2017

Printed by Halstan:
Halstan UK, 2–10 Plantation Road, Amersham, Bucks, HP6 6HJ. United Kingdom
Halstan DE, Weißliliengasse 4, 55116 Mainz. Germany

Copy editing and project management by Diana Greene-Sangaré
Music origination by The Note Factory

In *Double Bind?*, my desire is to offer, on the one hand, a glimpse of the inner life of sounds and, on the other hand, a fantasized, manipulated and altered view of the relationship between musician and instrument as well as life "in the wings" of a musician.

As in my preceding work for live instruments and electronics, I have taken an interest here in the playful jumble of the limits between the "real" and the "artificial".

Unsuk Chin
December 2007

---

*Double Bind?* was premiered on 2 December 2007
at the Théâtre des Bouffes du Nord in Paris
by Hae-Sun Kang, for whom the work was written.

The live electronics were designed by Benoit Meudic at IRCAM.

---

To obtain the IRCAM-controlled electronic portion of this work as well as further instructions regarding hardware requirements and setup; installation of the microphones; and patch documentation, please email Boosey & Hawkes in the first instance for relevant contact details (composers@boosey.com).

## Performance note

At the start of the piece, the violinist is nonchalantly leaning against a bar stool. The violin is held upright and rests on the violinist's knees. The strokes on the initial string with an old, well-worn piece of scouring pad are slow and, after each one, a soft, circular motion brings the hand back to the starting position. The violinist has a relaxed attitude.

The four principal techniques used in this piece begin at rehearsal letter **B**: shaking/moving the violin, fingering noise, tapping the strings with the fingers of the right hand and left-hand *pizzicato*. When moving and shaking the violin, the player should seem perplexed. (Shake it near his ear; turn it upside down, etc.)

Just before rehearsal letter **C**, the violinist takes the bow then begins stroking the E string again with the used piece of scouring pad, all the while slowly bringing the violin to its normal position. He then begins a series of *glissandi* and harmonics. This section ends with a horizontal glissando of the bow towards the nut, not unlike a crushing caress.

At rehearsal letter **D**, the previously used techniques continue with the addition of notes *col legno battuto*. At the end of this section, the violinist puts down the bow and stands up. He then shakes the violin here, there and everywhere for 25 seconds. The movements – which trigger various electronic effects – become increasingly agitated; the violinist seems increasingly perplexed.

Section **E** consists of a long, frenetic passage comprised of thumps on the body of the violin and fingering noises as well as right hand *pizzicati* and string taps. In the middle of this section, the violinist takes the bow and adds short, *arco* riffs to the mix. The section ends with a passage of approximately forty seconds during which the violinist beats the instrument more and more brutally before tapering down to a soft piano.

From rehearsal letter **F**, we have a few *glissandi* that lead to **G**, a series of scratching noises mingled with various riffs that hark back to the preceding sections (*col legno battuto*, left-hand *pizzicato*, fingering noise, etc.).

At rehearsal letter **H**, the violinist performs a series of soft *glissandi col legno battuto* before taking the violin by the nut and swinging it from left to right like a pendulum.

## Special notation

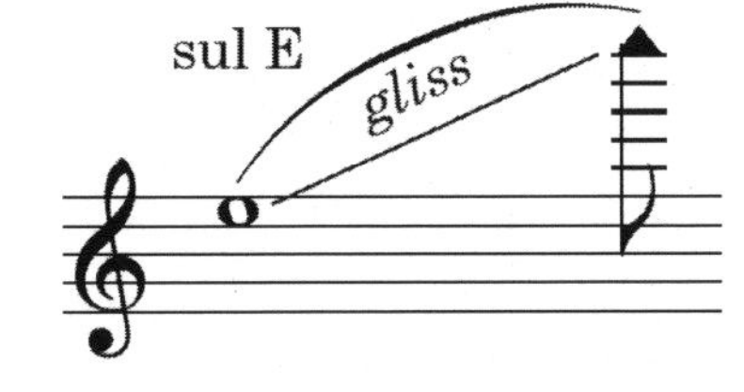


stroke the string with a piece of scouring pad, preferably well-worn

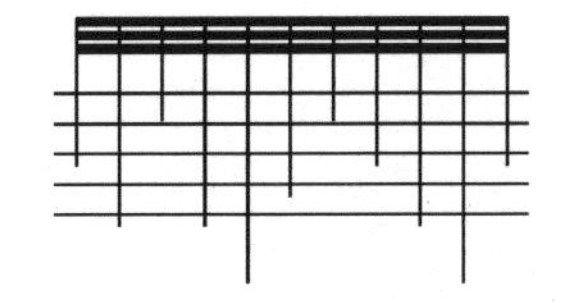

tap the strings with the fingers of the right hand

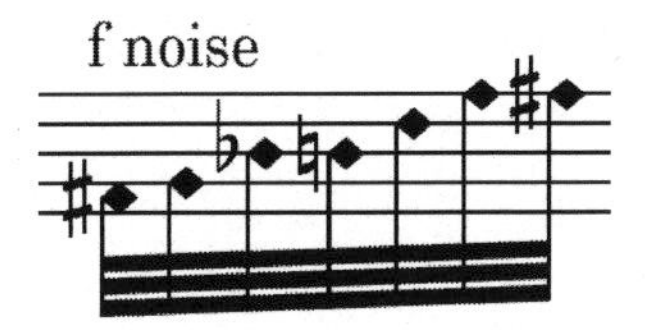


fingering noise

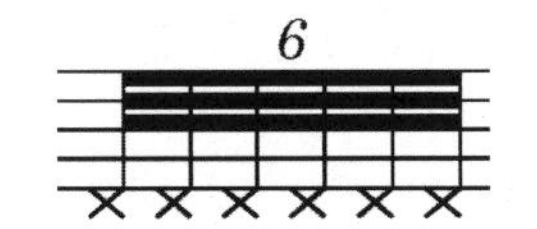


beat the body with fingers

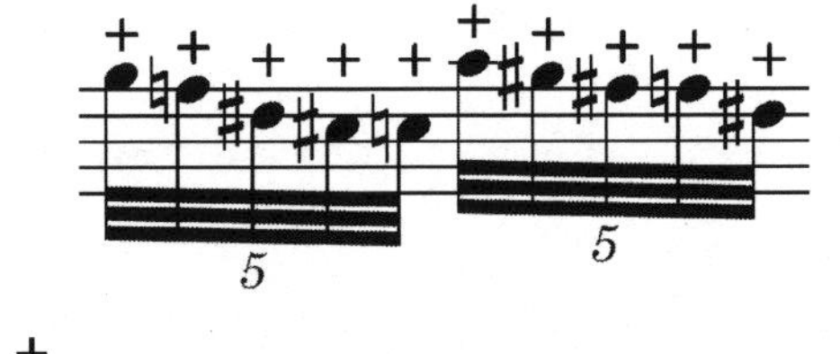


left-hand pizz

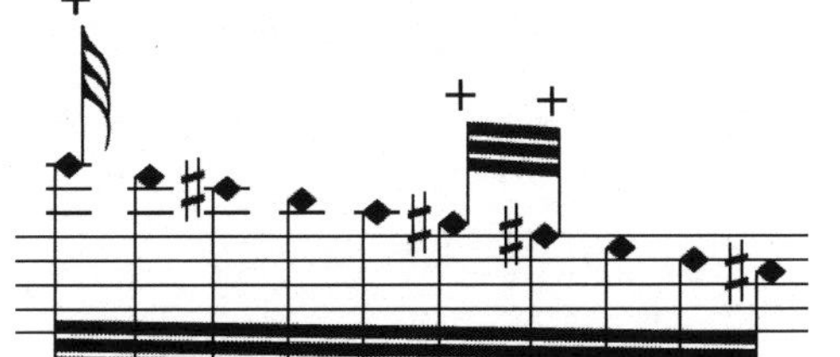

right-hand pizz (up-stemmed notes) in conjunction with fingering noise (down-stemmed notes)

## Electronic treatment details

letter A — Resonators escalate dynamically at each new event until **B**. The dynamics go from practically inaudible to very intrusive.

12 — The filters are turned off at the beginning so as not to pick up any noise when the violinist raises the instrument.

20 — file triggered manually when the violinist lowers the instrument then automatically triggered by the sensors from then on

22 — speed shift (electronic treatment)

30 — input interrupt

40 — resonators + harmonic filters (keep your hand on the controls)

60 — raindrops

65 — grains (samples captured and played back in real time)

70 — grains + (denser electronics)

75 — recorded samples triggered by the sensors as the violinist shakes and rotates the violin

85 — raindrops (+ continuing speed shift)

90 — denser

92 — even denser

95 — sound file (This file is heard when the violinist taps on the body of the violin. It is a long descent into the lower register that continues until there is no longer any sound. The tapping should continue until then.)

100 — resonators

120 — sound file that is triggered at the beginning of bar 2 after **G** and stops at the end of the second beat of the following bar

page 12 — The encircled letters represent the various electronic treatments:
A = granulation modulated by the amplitude envelope
D = granulation with transposition ramp (1200 in 20") + sound file
L = superimposition of samples triggered by attack detection
O = same as L
Q = same as L
S = stop
W = harmonizer
X = stop harmonizer
/ = sound file

160 — sound file

169 — Move the rotator of the mixing board to spatialize the sound file.

Dans *Double Bind?*, mon souhait est d'offrir, d'une part un aperçu de la vie intérieure des sons et, d'autre part, un regard fabulé, manipulé, altéré de la relation entre le musicien et l'instrument ainsi que de la vie « dans les coulisses » du musicien.

Comme dans mon œuvre précédente pour instruments live et électronique, je me suis intéressée ici à un enchevêtrement ludique des limites entre « le naturel » et « l'artifice ».

Unsuk Chin
décembre 2007

---

*Double Bind?* a été crée le 2 décembre 2007
au Théâtre des Bouffes du Nord à Paris
par Hae-Sun Kang, pour qui la pièce a été écrite.

La partie électroniqe a été réalisée par Benoit Meudic à l'IRCAM.

---

Pour obtenir la partie électronique de cette œuvre ainsi que plus de précisions concernant le matériel informatique et la préparation ; l'installation des microphones ; et la documentation sur le patch, merci de contacter Boosey & Hawkes dans un premier temps pour les coordonnées utiles (composers@boosey.com).

## Notes pour l'exécution

Au début de la pièce, le violoniste est debout mais s'appuie sur le bord d'un tabouret haut d'un air désinvolte. Le violon est tenu en position verticale et se repose sur ses genoux. Les caresses avec un bout de tampon à récurer se font lentement avec un mouvement doucement circulaire pour retourner au point de départ. L'attitude du violoniste est décontractée.

Au repère **B** commencent les quatre principales techniques de cette pièce: secouement du violon, bruit de doigté, tapotement des cordes avec les doigts de la main gauche et, un peu plus loin, *pizzicato* avec la main gauche. Les secouements du violon doivent être très variés et se faire d'un air perplexe.

Juste avant le repère **C**, le violoniste prend l'archet puis refait quelques caresses à la première corde du violon avec le morceau de tampon à récurer tout en ramenant le violon à sa position normale. Puis il entame un jeu de *glissando* et d'harmoniques. Cette partie se termine avec un *glissando* de l'archet, telle une caresse écrasée, vers la touche.

Au repère **D**, les techniques utilisées auparavant continuent avec l'ajout des notes *col legno battuto*. À la fin de cette partie, le violoniste pose l'archet et se met debout. Puis il secoue le violon dans tous les sens pendant 25 secondes. Les secouements – qui déclencheront des effets électroniques – seront de plus en plus rapides; le violoniste aura l'air de plus en plus perplexe.

La partie **E** consiste à un long passage rapide et frénétique composé de tapements sur le corps du violon et bruits de doigté ainsi que *pizzicati* et tapotements avec la main droite. Vers le milieu de cette section, le violoniste prend l'archet et ajoute des courts groupements de notes *arco* au reste. Le tout se termine avec un passage d'une quarantaine de secondes pendant lequel le violoniste frappe l'instrument de plus en plus brutalement avant de diminuer la vitesse et le volume des tapements.

La partie **F** est composée de quelques *glissandi* qui mènent au repère **G**, une série de bruits d'éraflures intercalées avec quelques riffs rappelant les passages précédents (*col legno battuto*, *pizzicato* main gauche, bruits de doigté, etc.).

Au repère **H**, le violoniste effectue quelques doux *glissandi col legno battuto* avant de prendre le violon par le sillet et de le balancer de gauche à droite comme une pendule.

## Notations spécifiques

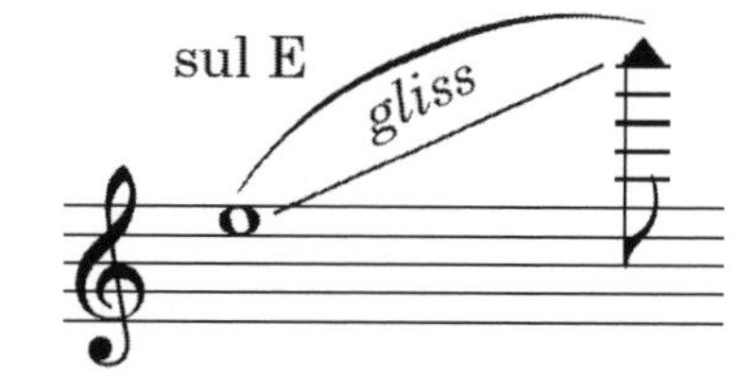


caresser la corde avec un morceau de tampon à récurer, de préférence bien usé

effleurer les cordes avec les doigts de la main droite

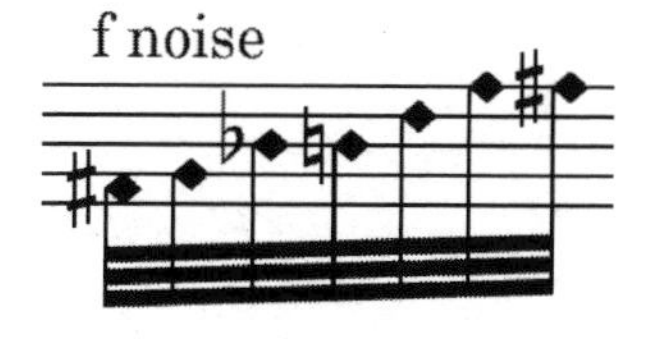


bruit de doigté

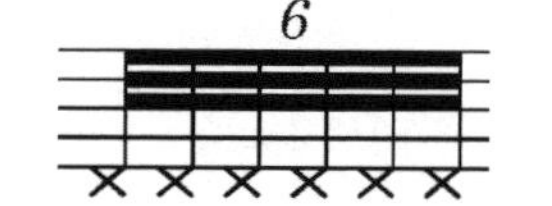


frapper la table avec les doigts

pizz main gauche

pizz main droite (hampes en haut) conjointement avec des bruits de doigté (hampes en bas)

## Précisions sur le traitement électronique

repère A — Filtres résonnants *(resonators)* en crescendo à chaque nouvel évènement jusqu'à **B**. Dynamique allant du presque imperceptible au très présent.

12 — Les filtres sont coupés en entrée pour ne pas récupérer les bruits lorsque l'instrumentiste lève l'instrument.

20 — fichier déclenché manuellement lorsque l'instrumentiste baisse le violon puis ouverture du déclenchement des échantillons enregistrés par les capteurs

22 — *speed shift* (traitement électronique)

30 — coupure de l'entrée

40 — résonateurs + filtres harmoniques (garder la main sur les niveaux)

60 — gouttes de pluie *(raindrops)*

65 — grains (échantillons capturés et rediffusés en temps réel)

70 — grains + (électronique plus dense)

75 — échantillons enregistrés déclenchés par les capteurs (secouements et rotations du violon)

85 — raindrops (+ *speed shift* qui continue)

90 — plus dense

92 — encore plus dense

95 — fichier son (Ce fichier son s'entend lorsque le violoniste tape sur le corps du violon. Il s'agit d'une longue descente dans le grave qui continue jusqu'à ce qu'il n'y ait plus de son. Les tapotements doivent continuer jusqu'alors.)

100 — filtres résonnants

120 — fichier son qui est déclenché à la mesure 2 et qui s'arrête à la fin du deuxième temps de la mesure suivante

page 12 — Les lettres indiquent les ouvertures et fermetures des différents traitements électroniques:
A = granulation modulée par l'enveloppe d'amplitude
D = granulation avec rampe de transposition 1200 en 20s + fichier son
L = superposition d'échantillons déclenchés par détection d'attaque
O = idem que L
Q = idem que L
S = arrêt
W = harmonizer
X = arrêter harmonizer
/ = fichier son

160 — fichier son

169 — Déplacer le rotateur de la table de mixage afin de spatialiser le fichier son.

In *Double Bind? [Doppelbund?]* versuche ich einerseits, einen Einblick in das Innenleben von Klängen zu gewähren, und andererseits, eine imaginäre, manipulierte und veränderte Vorstellung von der Beziehung zwischen Musiker und Instrument sowie vom Leben „hinter der Bühne" eines Musikers zu geben.

Wie in meinem vorangegangenen Werk für akustische Instrumente und Elektronik interessierte ich mich auch hier für das spielerische Durcheinander bei der Abgrenzung des „Realen" von dem „Artifiziellen".

Unsuk Chin
Dezember 2007

---

Die Uraufführung von *Double Bind? [Doppelbund?]* fand am 2. Dezember 2007 im Théâtre des Bouffes du Nord in Paris durch Hae-Sun Kang statt, für den das Werk geschrieben wurde.

Die Live-Elektronik wurde von Benoit Meudic am IRCAM eingerichtet.

---

Für den von IRCAM geschützten elektronischen Teil dieses Werkes sowie für weitere Hinweise zu den Anforderungen an die Hardware und ihre Anordnung, zur Installation der Mikrophone und für die Patchdokumentation schicken Sie bitte zuerst eine E-Mail an Boosey & Hawkes für relevante Kontaktinformationen (composers@boosey.com).

## Aufführungshinweis

Zu Beginn des Stückes lehnt sich der/die ViolinistIn nonchalant gegen einen Barstuhl. Die Violine wird aufrecht gehalten und ruht auf den Knien des/der Violinisten/Violinistin. Die Streichelbewegungen auf der ersten Saite mit einem alten, sehr abgenutzten Topfkratzer geschehen langsam. Nach jedem Streicheln bringt eine sanfte Kreisbewegung die Hand zurück zur Ausgangsposition. Der/die ViolinistIn gibt sich entspannt.

Die vier Grundtechniken, die in diesem Stück zur Anwendung kommen, beginnen bei dem Probenbuchstaben **B**: die Violine schütteln/bewegen, Griffgeräusch, die Saiten mit den Fingern der rechten Hand antippen und Pizzikato der linken Hand. Beim Bewegen und Schütteln der Violine sollte der/die ViolinistIn aussehen, als sei er/sie verwirrt (das Instrument nahe am Ohr schütteln, auf den Kopf stellen usw.).

Kurz vor dem Probenbuchstaben **C** nimmt der/die ViolinistIn den Bogen auf, beginnt dann die E-Saite wieder mit dem abgenutzten Topfkratzer zu streicheln, während der/die InterpretIn gleichzeitig die Violine langsam in ihre normale Lage bringt. Er/sie beginnt dann mit einer Reihe von Glissandi und Flageoletts. Dieser Abschnitt endet mit einem horizontalen Glissando des Bogens in Richtung Wirbelkasten, was einem liebkosenden Drücken nicht unähnlich ist.

Bei dem Probenbuchstaben **D** werden neben schon zuvor verwendeten Techniken auch Noten *col legno battuto* gespielt. Am Ende dieses Abschnitts legt der/die ViolinistIn den Bogen zur Seite und steht auf. Daraufhin schüttelt der/die InterpretIn die Violine 25 Sekunden in alle möglichen Richtungen. Die Bewegungen – die verschiedene elektronische Effekte auslösen – werden zunehmend aufgeregter. Der/die ViolinistIn scheint zunehmend verwirrt.

Abschnitt **E** enthält eine lange, frenetische Passage, die aus dumpfen Schlägen gegen den Resonanzkörper der Violine, aus Griffgeräuschen, Pizzikati der rechten Hand und Antippen der Saiten besteht. In der Mitte dieses Abschnitts nimmt der/die ViolinistIn den Bogen und fügt dem Gemisch kurze, *arco* gespielte Riffs hinzu. Der Abschnitt endet mit einer Passage von ungefähr 40 Sekunden, in der der/die ViolinistIn das Instrument immer stärker brutal schlägt. Danach geht er/sie auf ein weiches Piano zurück.

Ab dem Probenbuchstaben **F** haben wir einige Glissandi, die zu **G** führen, eine Reihe kratzender Geräusche gemischt mit diversen Riffs, die an vorangegangene Abschnitte erinnern (*col legno battuto*, Pizzikato der linken Hand, Griffgeräusch usw.).

Bei dem Probenbuchstaben **H** führt der/die ViolinistIn eine Reihe weicher Glissandi *col legno battuto* aus. Danach greift er/sie die Violine am Wirbelkasten und schwingt sie von links nach rechts wie ein Pendel.

## Spezielle Notation

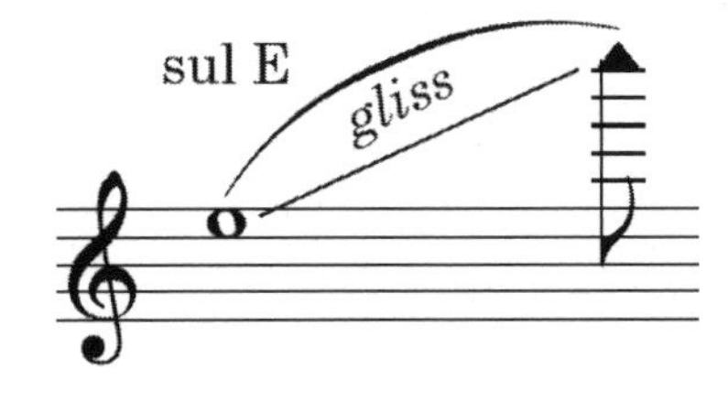


die Saite mit einem Topfkratzer streicheln, vorzugsweise mit einem sehr abgenutzten

die Saiten mit den Fingern der rechten Hand antippen

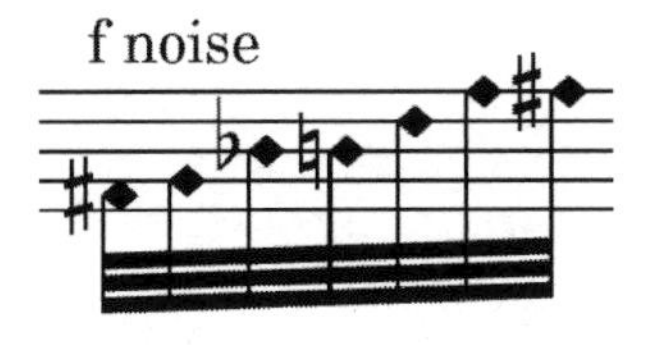


Griffgeräusch

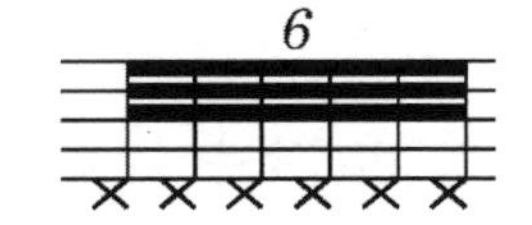


den Körper mit Fingern schlagen

Pizzikato mit der linken Hand

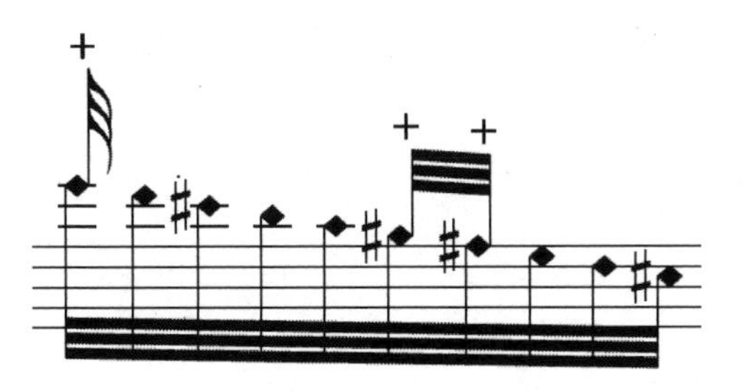

Pizzikato mit der rechten Hand (Noten mit Notenhals nach oben) zusammen mit Griffgeräusch (Noten mit Notenhals nach unten)

## Hinweise zur elektronischen Behandlung

Buchstabe A — Resonatoren werden bis **B** bei jedem neuen Ereignis immer lauter. Die Lautstärke erstreckt sich von so gut wie unhörbar bis zu sehr zudringlich.

12 — Die Filter sind zu Beginn ausgeschaltet, damit kein Geräusch aufgenommen wird, während der/die ViolinistIn das Instrument anhebt.

20 — Der Clip ist manuell auszulösen, wenn der/die ViolinistIn das Instrument senkt, dann wird er durch die Sensoren automatisch ausgelöst und bleibt an.

22 — Tempoumschaltung (elektronische Behandlung)

30 — Inputunterbrechung

40 — Resonatoren + Harmoniefilter (Hände auf den Reglern halten)

60 — Regentropfen

65 — Körner (aufgenommene Samples werden in Echtzeit abgespielt)

70 — Körner + (dichtere elektronische Klänge)

75 — Aufgenommene Samples werden durch die Sensoren ausgelöst, während der/die ViolinistIn die Violine schüttelt und dreht.

85 — Regentropfen (+ anhaltende Tempoumschaltung)

90 — dichter

92 — noch dichter

95 — Audio-Clip (Dieser Audio-Clip ist zu hören, wenn der/die ViolinistIn den Körper der Violine antippt. Es ist ein langer Abstieg in das tiefere Register, der andauert, bis es keinen Klang mehr gibt. Das Tippen sollte so lange weitergehen.)

100 — Resonatoren

120 — Audio-Clip, der zu Beginn des 2. Takts nach **G** ausgelöst wird und am Ende der 2. Zählzei des darauf folgenden Takts endet.

Seite 12 — Die eingekreisten Buchstaben verweisen auf die unterschiedlichen elektronischen Behandlungen:

- A = durch die Amplitudenhüllkurve modulierte Granulation
- D = Granulation mit Transponierrampe (1200 in 20") + Audio-Clip
- L = Überlagerung von Samples, die durch Erkennung des Spieleinsatzes aus gelöst werden
- O = das Gleiche wie L
- Q = das Gleiche wie L
- S = halt
- W = Harmonizer
- X = Harmonizer stoppen
- / = Audio-Clip

160 — Audio-Clip

169 — Die Rotationsfunktion des Mischpults anwenden, um dem Audio-Clip einen Raumef fekt zu geben.

*duration: 17 minutes*

---

*durée: 17 minutes*

---

*Spieldauer: 17 Minuten*

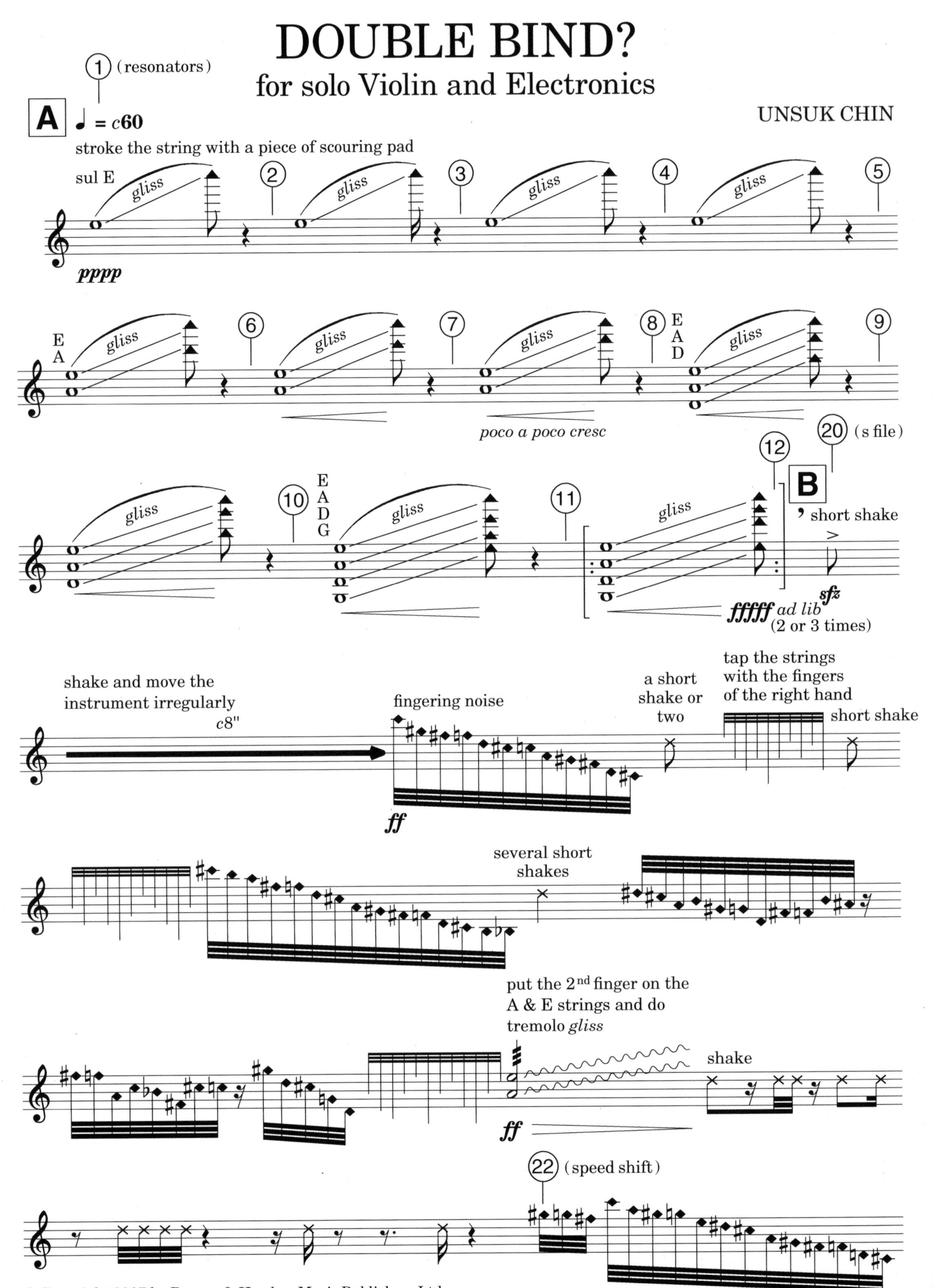
DOUBLE BIND?
for solo Violin and Electronics
UNSUK CHIN
1 (resonators)
A ♩ = c60
stroke the string with a piece of scouring pad
sul E
gliss
pppp
2
3
4
5
E A
6
7
8
E A D
9
poco a poco cresc
E A D G
10
11
12
20 (s file)
B
short shake
sfz
fffff ad lib (2 or 3 times)
shake and move the instrument irregularly
c8"
fingering noise
ff
a short shake or two
tap the strings with the fingers of the right hand
short shake
several short shakes
put the 2nd finger on the A & E strings and do tremolo gliss
shake
ff
22 (speed shift)

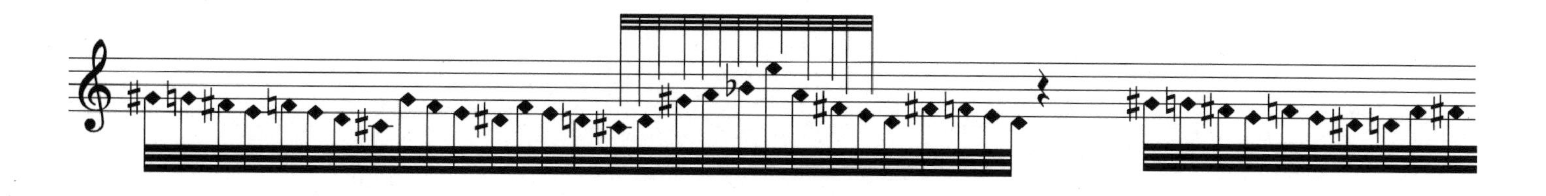

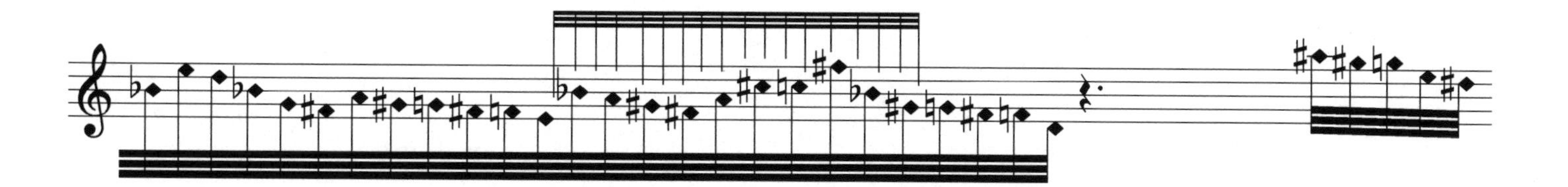

LH pizz

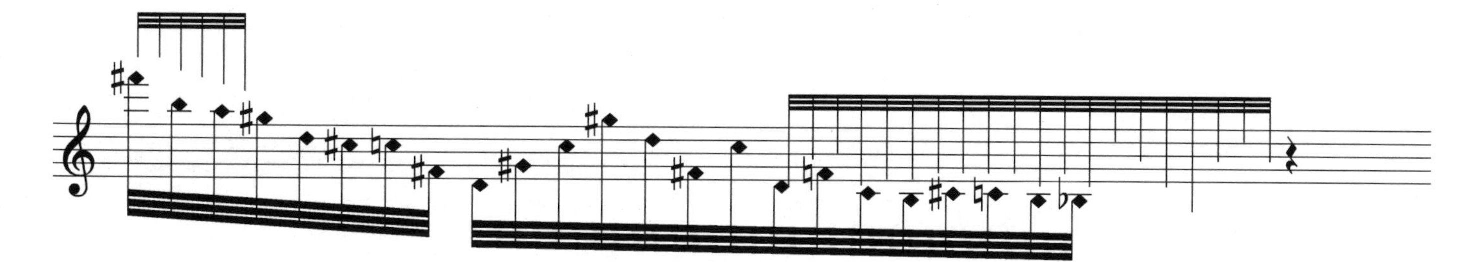

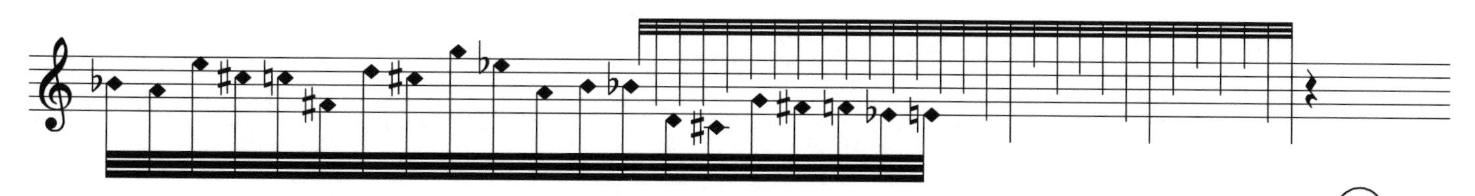

take the bow
30 (stop)

40 (harmonic filters)
C
stroke with a piece of scouring pad
repeat, and in the meantime bring the
instrument to the ordinary position
gliss
ppp
4x
42
arco
sul E
44
45
c15"
pppp
sul A
E
47
5"
sul A
sul E
49
c8"
c5"
sul G
sul D
poco a poco cresc
60 (raindrops)
press the bow on the strings
and stroke slowly crossways
D
♩ = c80
ord
fff
mf
f

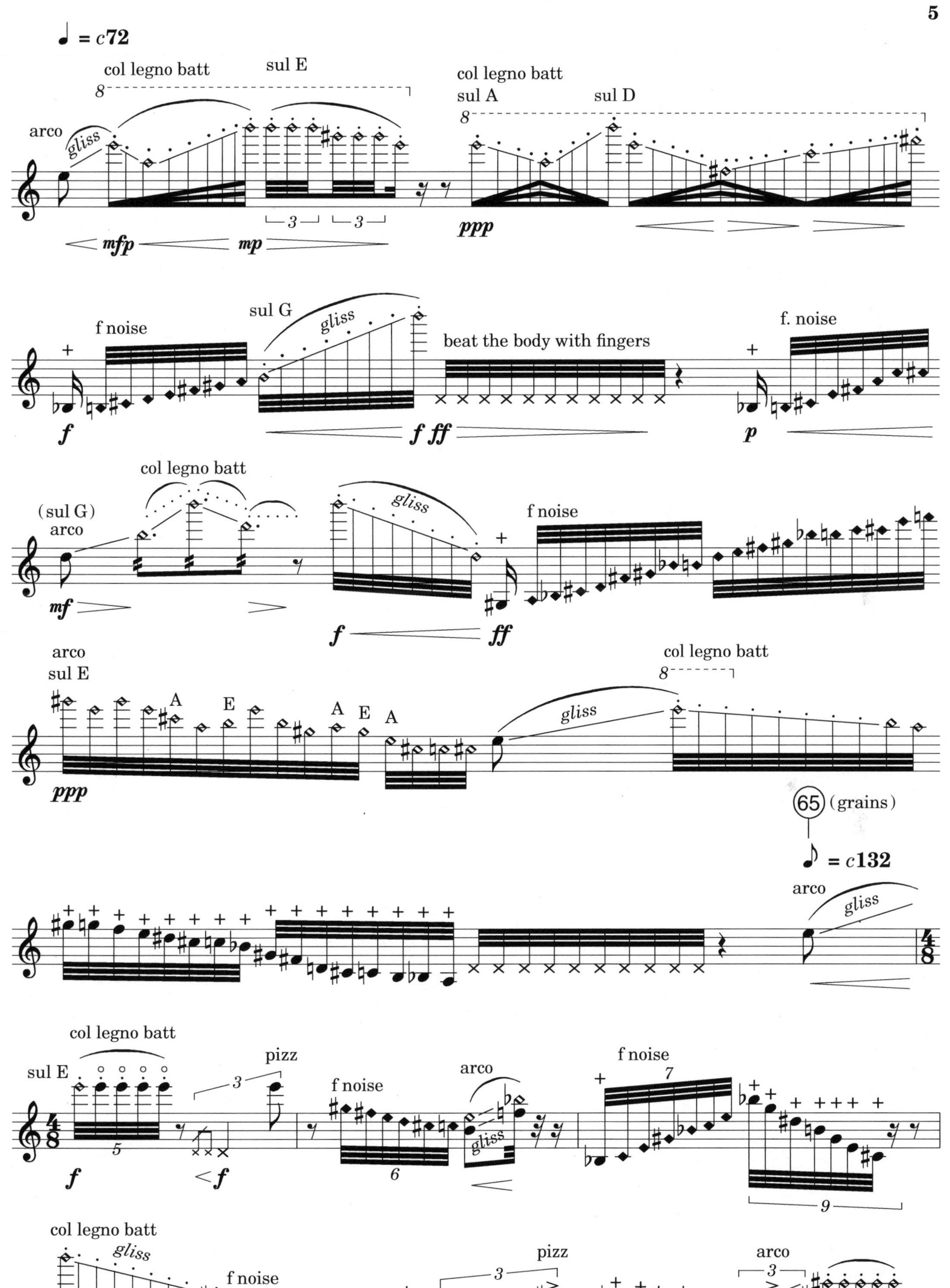
♩ = c72
col legno batt
sul E
arco
gliss
mfp
mp
col legno batt
sul A
sul D
ppp
f noise
sul G
gliss
beat the body with fingers
f ff
f. noise
p
col legno batt
(sul G)
arco
mf
gliss
f noise
f
ff
arco
sul E
A
E
ppp
col legno batt
gliss
65 (grains)
♪ = c132
arco
gliss

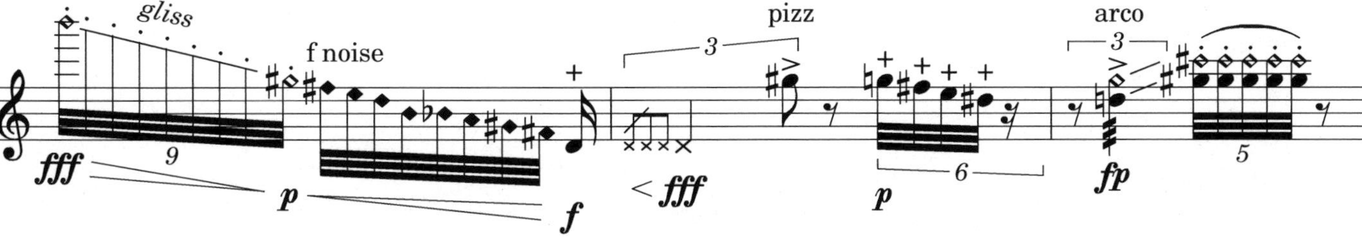
col legno batt
sul E
pizz
f noise
arco
f noise
gliss
col legno batt
gliss
f noise
fff
p
f
pizz
fff
arco
fp

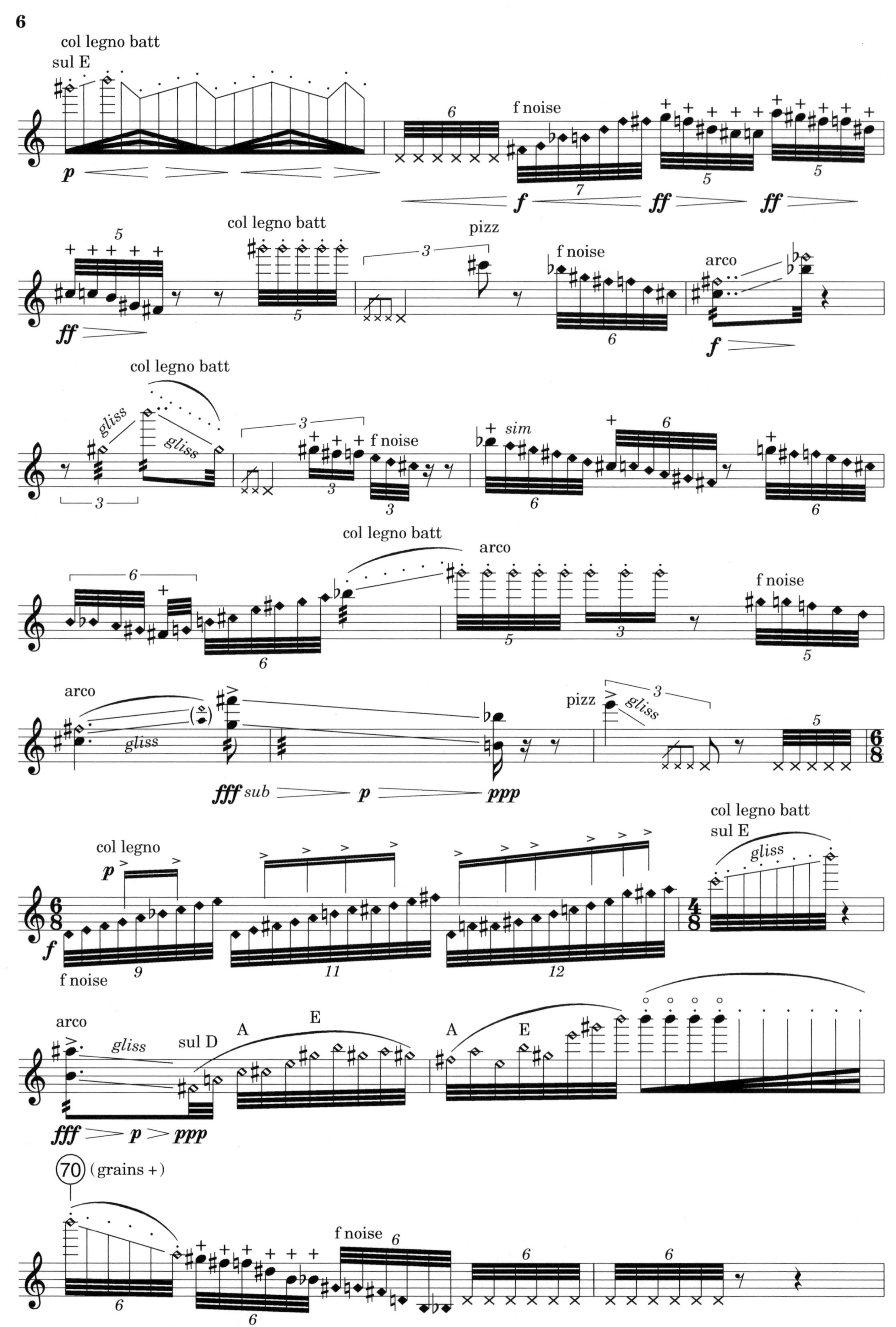
col legno batt
sul E
p
6
f noise
7
5
f
ff
ff
5
col legno batt
5
3
pizz
f noise
6
arco
f
col legno batt
gliss
gliss
3
3
3
f noise
3
sim
6
6
6
6
col legno batt
arco
6
5
3
f noise
5
arco
gliss
fff sub
p
ppp
pizz
gliss
3
5
col legno
p
f
f noise
9
11
12
col legno batt
sul E
gliss
arco
gliss
sul D
A
E
A
E
fff
p
ppp
70
(grains +)
6
6
f noise
6
6
6

sul A
arco
col legno batt
pizz
arco
gliss
f noise
clb
sul A
f noise
pizz
arco
fpp
mf
ppp
clb
sul E
f
mp
ppp
f noise
f noise
arco flautando
f
fff
cresc with pressure
on string - slow bow
clb
pizz
arco
gliss
p
ppp
gliss
f
A
E
A
E
gliss
gliss
pizz
fingering noise
75
(s file)
25"
shake and move the instrument
in an increasingly rapid fashion
put the bow
down and stand up
cresc

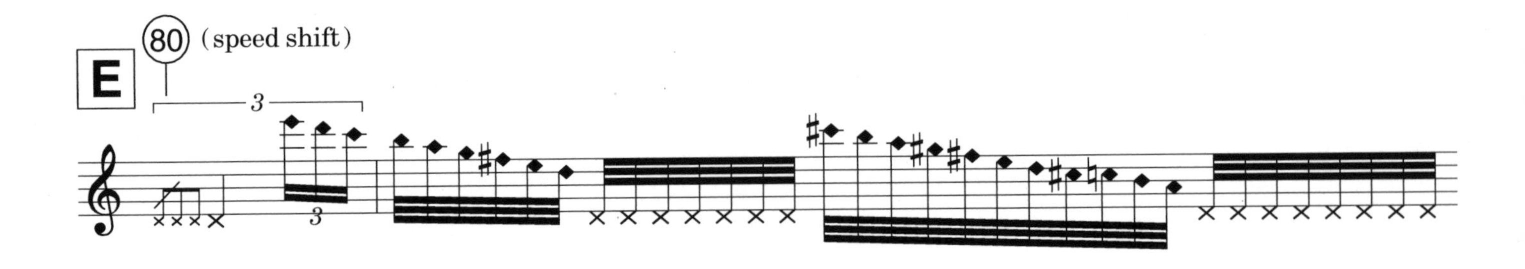
E
80
(speed shift)
3
3

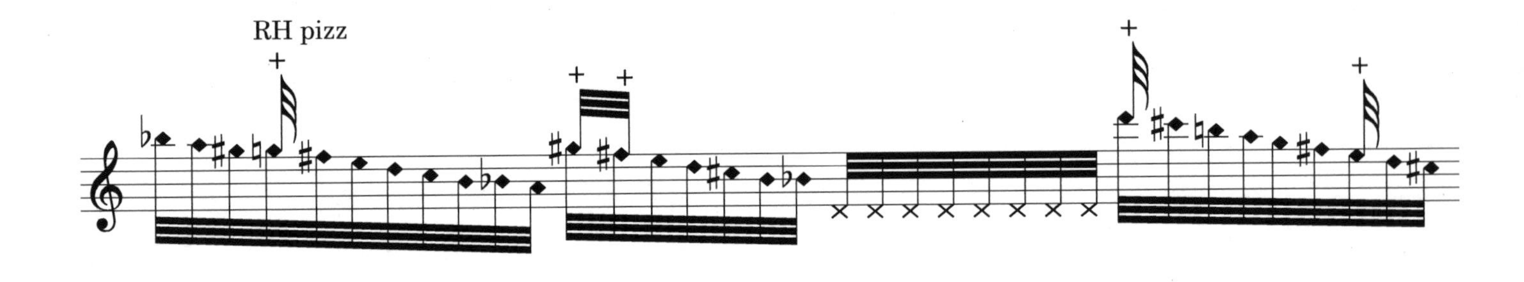
RH pizz

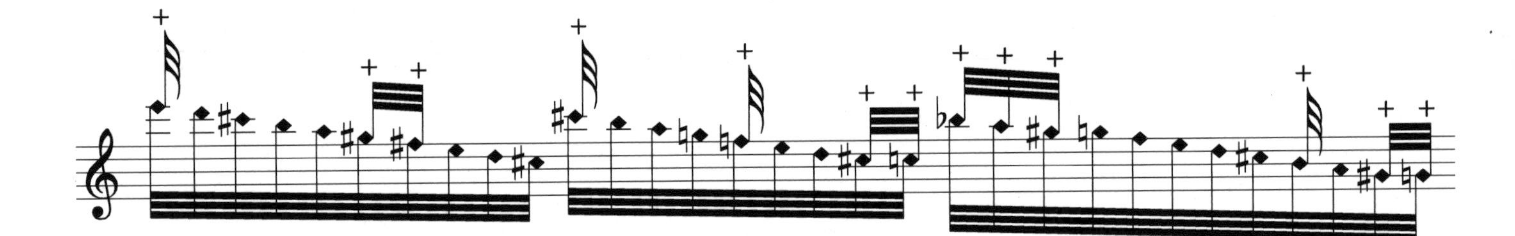

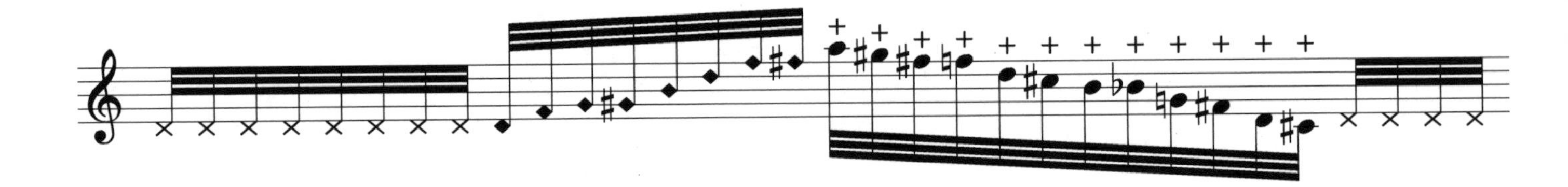

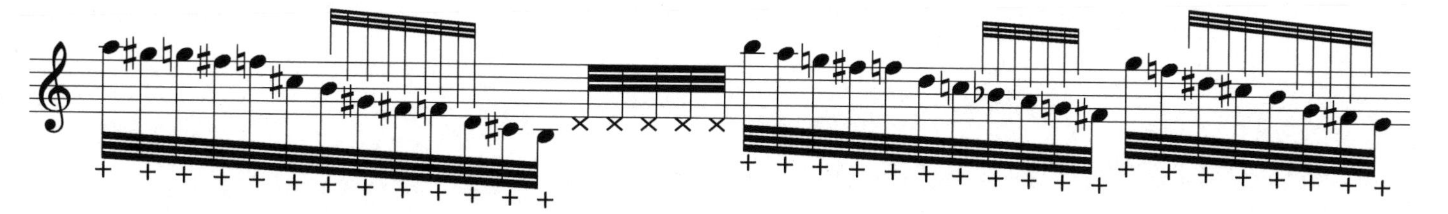

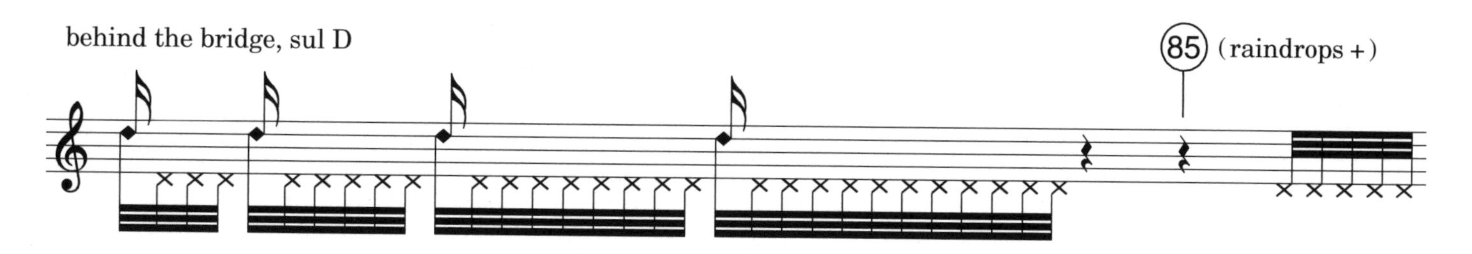
behind the bridge, sul D
85
(raindrops +)

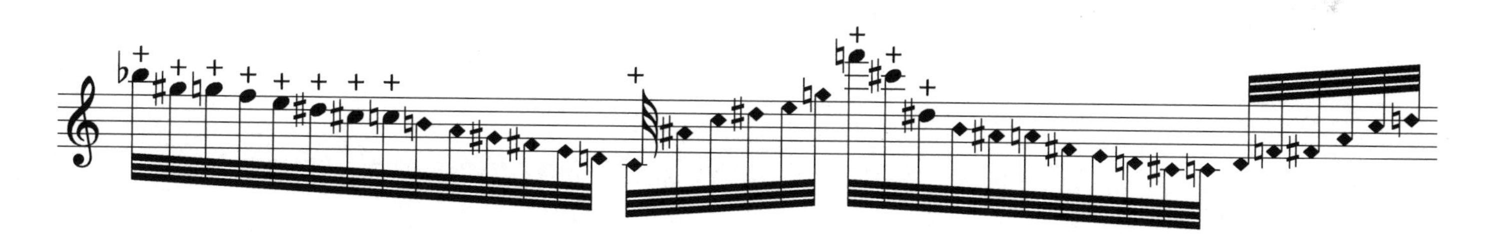

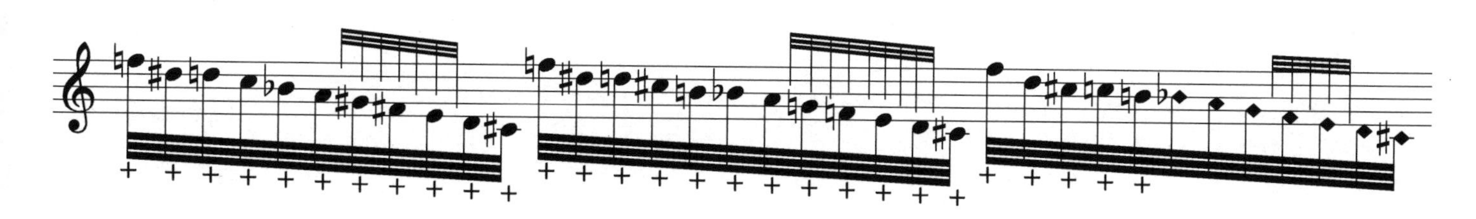

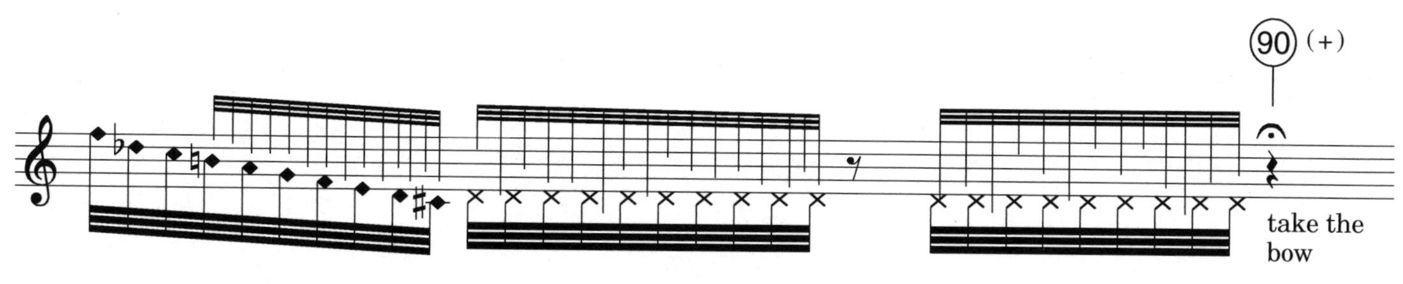
90
(+)
take the bow

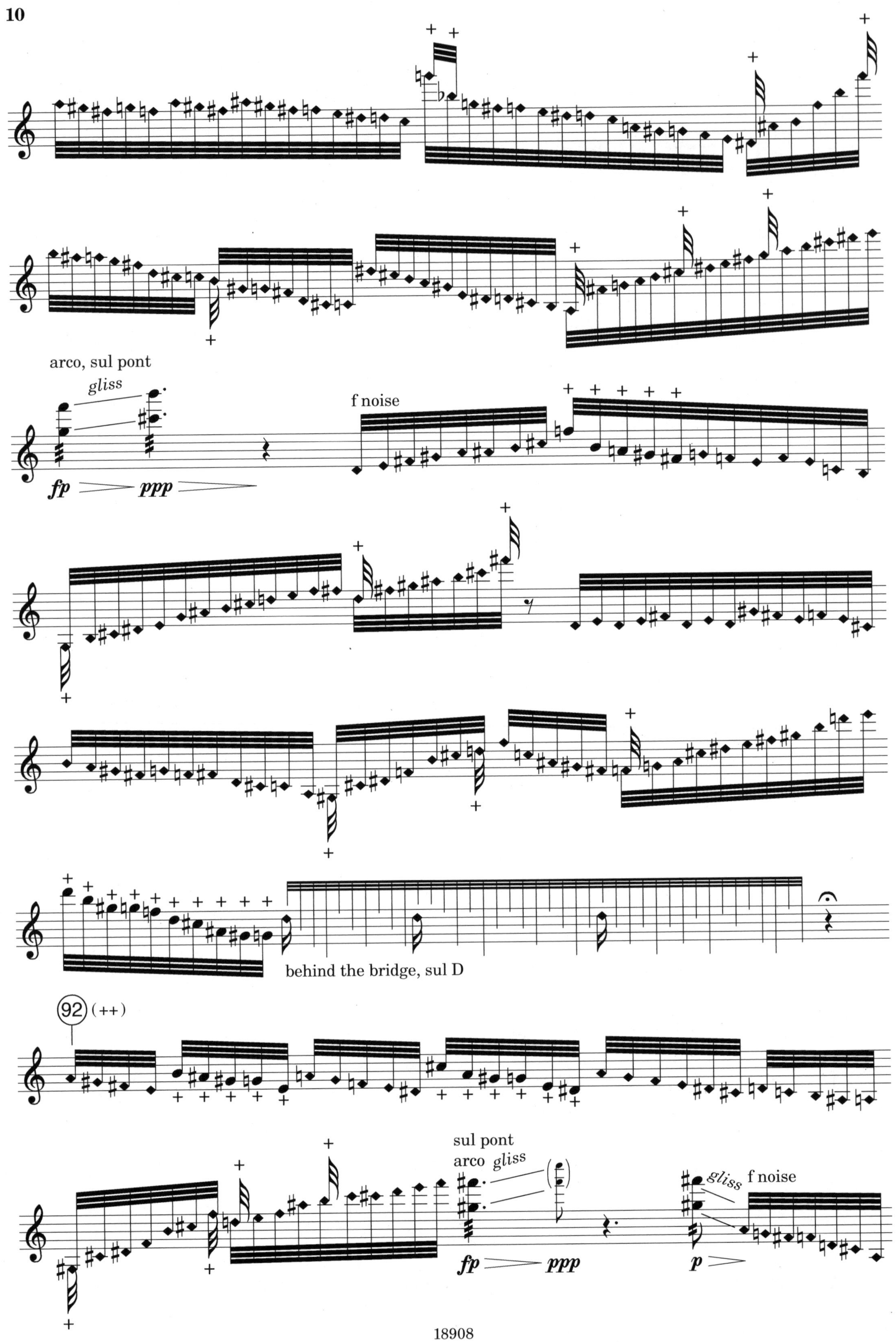
arco, sul pont
gliss
fp
ppp
f noise
behind the bridge, sul D
92
(++)
sul pont
arco
gliss
fp
ppp
gliss
f noise
p

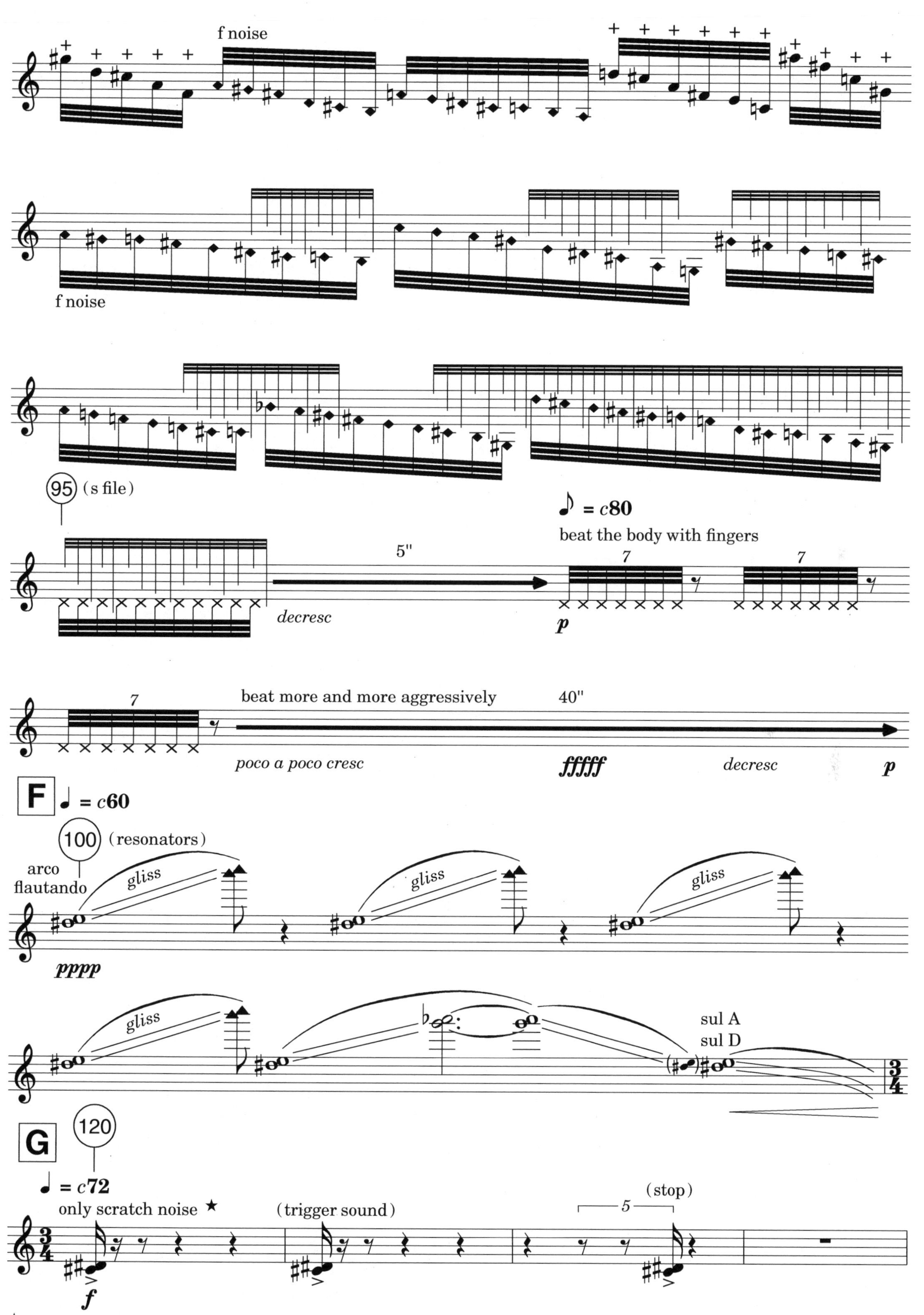
f noise
f noise
95 (s file)
5"
decresc
♪ = c80
beat the body with fingers
7
p
7
7
beat more and more aggressively
40"
poco a poco cresc
fffff
decresc
p
F
♩ = c60
100 (resonators)
arco
flautando
gliss
pppp
sul A
sul D
G
120
♩ = c72
only scratch noise ★
(trigger sound)
5
(stop)
f
★bow remains on the strings after scratching

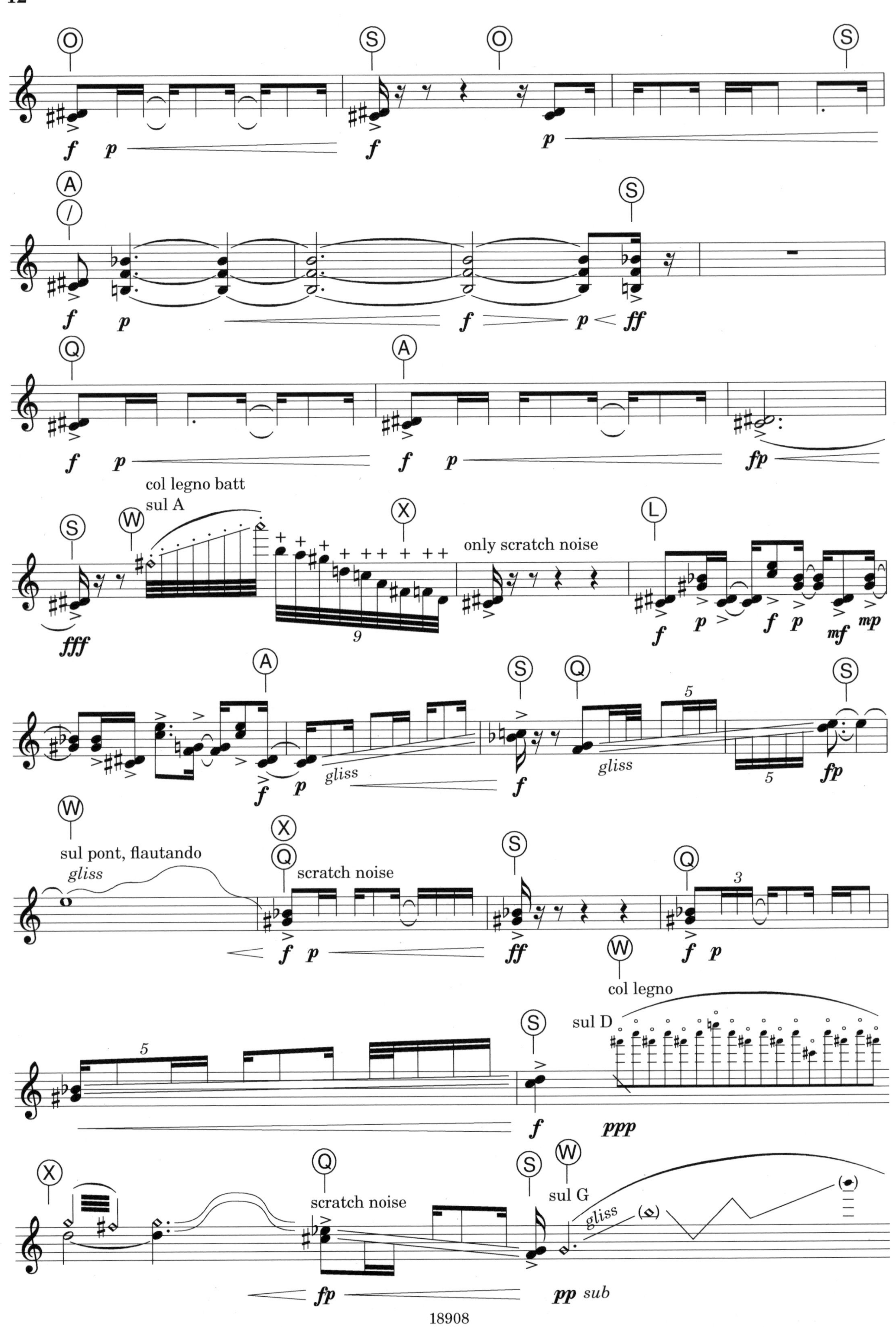
col legno batt
sul A
only scratch noise
gliss
sul pont, flautando
gliss
scratch noise
col legno
sul D
scratch noise
sul G
gliss
pp sub

clb
f noise
arco
sul pont
flautando
f
f
pppp
f
Q
8
col
legno
sul A
scratch noise
X
/
A
S
ppp
gliss
fp
mf
W
col legno
X
Q
scratch noise
A
pppp
mf
f
p
p
D
3
5
ff
decresc
ppp
♪ = c80
H
160
(s file)
clb
sul D
(8)
(8)
sul G
(8)
169
20"
take the violin by the nut and swing it
from left to right like a pendulum

# Glossary / Lexique / Glossar

| English | français | Deutsch |
|---|---|---|
| *Page 2* | *Page 2* | *Seite 2* |
| stroke the string with a piece of scouring pad | caresser la corde avec un morceau de tampon à récurer | die Saite mit einem Topfkratzer streicheln |
| s file (sound file) | fichier son | A-Clip (Audio-Clip) |
| short shake | secousse brève | kurzes Schütteln |
| 2 or 3 times | 2 ou 3 fois | 2 oder 3 Mal |
| shake and move the instrument irregularly | secouer et bouger l'instrument de façon irrégulière | das Instrument unregelmäßig schütteln und bewegen |
| fingering noise | bruit de doigté | Griffgeräusch |
| a short shake or two | une secousse brève ou deux | ein- oder zweimal kurz schütteln |
| tap the strings with the fingers of the right hand | tapper les cordes avec les doigts de la main droite | die Saiten mit den Fingern der rechte Hand antippen |
| several short shakes | plusieurs secousses brèves | mehrmals kurz schütteln |
| put the 2nd finger on the A & E strings and do tremolo *gliss* | mettre le 2e doigt sur les cordes La et Mi et faire un trémolo *gliss* | den 2. Finger auf die A- und E-Saite legen und ein tremolierendes Glissando ausführen |
| speed shift | changement de vitesse | Tempoumschaltung |
| *Page 3* | *Page 3* | *Seite 3* |
| take the bow | prendre l'archet | den Bogen aufnehmen |
| stop | arrêt | halt |
| *Page 4* | *Page 4* | *Seite 4* |
| stroke with a piece of scouring pad, repeat, and in the meantime bring the instrument to the ordinary position | caresser avec un morceau de tampon à récurer et répéter tout en ramenant l'instrument à sa position normale | mit einem Topfkratzer streicheln, wiederholen und dabei das Instrument in die gewöhnliche Lage bringen |
| press the bow on the strings and stroke slowly crossways | appuyer sur les cordes avec l'archet et les caresser lentement en travers | den Bogen auf die Saiten drücken und langsam quer hinüberschieben |
| raindrops | gouttes de pluie | Regentropfen |
| *Page 5* | *Page 5* | *Seite 5* |
| beat the body with fingers | frapper la table avec les doigts | mit Fingern auf den Resonanzkörper schlagen |
| *Page 7* | *Page 7* | *Seite 7* |
| *cresc* with pressure on string - slow bow | *cresc* avec pression sur la corde - archet lent | *crescendo* mit Druck auf der Saite – langsame Bogenführung |
| shake and move the instrument in an increasingly rapid fashion | secouer et bouger l'instrument de plus en plus rapidement | das Instrument zunehmend kräftig schütteln und bewegen |
| put the bow down and stand up | poser l'archet et se mettre debout | den Bogen weglegen und aufstehen |
| *Page 11* | *Page 11* | *Seite 11* |
| beat more and more aggressively | frappements de plus en plus aggressifs | zunehmend aggressiv schlagen |
| only scratch noise | bruit d'éraflure uniquement | nur Kratzgeräusch |
| trigger sound | enclencher le son | Audio-Clip auslösen |
| *Page 13* | *Page 13* | *Seite 13* |
| take the violin by the nut and swing it from the left to the right like a pendulum | prendre le violon par le sillet et le balancer de gauche à droite comme une pendule | die Violine am Wirbelkasten greifen und von links nach rechts wie ein Pendel schwingen |